William's Sk[ateboard]

William got a skateboard for
his birthday.
2

William said, "I don't like skateboards."

Mom went for a ride on
William's skateboard.

4

"You take a turn William,"
said Mom.

"No," said William. "I don't want to."

6

Dad went for a ride on
William's skateboard.

"You take a turn William,"
said Dad.

"No," said William. "I don't
want to."

9

Grandma said, "I'll have a
turn."

10

Grandma went whizzing
down the hill on William's
skateboard.

"That was fun," shouted
Grandma.

"I'm going to have another turn."

"No," said William. "It's my
turn."

William went whizzing down
the hill ...

... again and again and again.